FINGER PAINTING

Dip your finger in water,
pick a color. Then apply
your fingerprint onto the paper
to complete the illustrations.

Use a damp cloth to clean
your fingers before switching
to a different color.

Come and play with us!

Use your thumb to create
large circles and your other
fingers for smaller circles.

The paint palette provided with the book
will help you do the exercises.
Don't hesitate to use other colors.

To color in larger areas you
may have to apply your
fingerprints several times.

In the tropical forest

Add some colored spots
on the snakes.

Complete the chameleon
with different colors.

Add some color on
the turtles' shells.

The Indians

Add some color on the teepee.

Just like the Indians, make some smoke signals!

Add some leaves on the bushes.

Decorate the teepees
with beautiful colors!

The Martians Invasion

Color in
the planets
with your thumb.

Finish the spaceships.

Create the Martians' bodies with your fingerprints.

Add some colors on the star.

Dab your thumb
in the yellow paint and
color in the window.

Complete the green
little aliens.

In the Garden

Add some colors on the butterflies wings.

Dab your finger in your paint and color the flower.

Complete the bee's body
with yellow fingerprints.

Dab your finger in the blue paint
and draw the bee's wings.

Add some petals with
your thumb. Place your
fingerprint in the flower.

The Princesses

Color in the princesses' dresses with your thumb.

Make beautiful hearts
with 2 fingerprints
in each heart.

Complete the dog and the 2 dresses.

Toys

Put your fingerprints
on the stuffed animals and
the dolls to finish them.

Complete the flower.

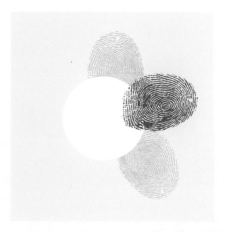

Add some balls
on the bookshelf
with your fingerprints.

Add some colors on the train.

At the bottom of the ocean

Add different colored spots on the octopus.

Dab your finger in the blue paint and add bubbles.

Finish
these little fish with
your fingerprints.

Add some spots
on the big fish.

The robots

Complete the giant robot with your fingerprints.

Color the inside of the wheels.

Color in each little robot in a different way.

The cavemen

Dab your finger
in the blue paint
to color in the
snowflakes.

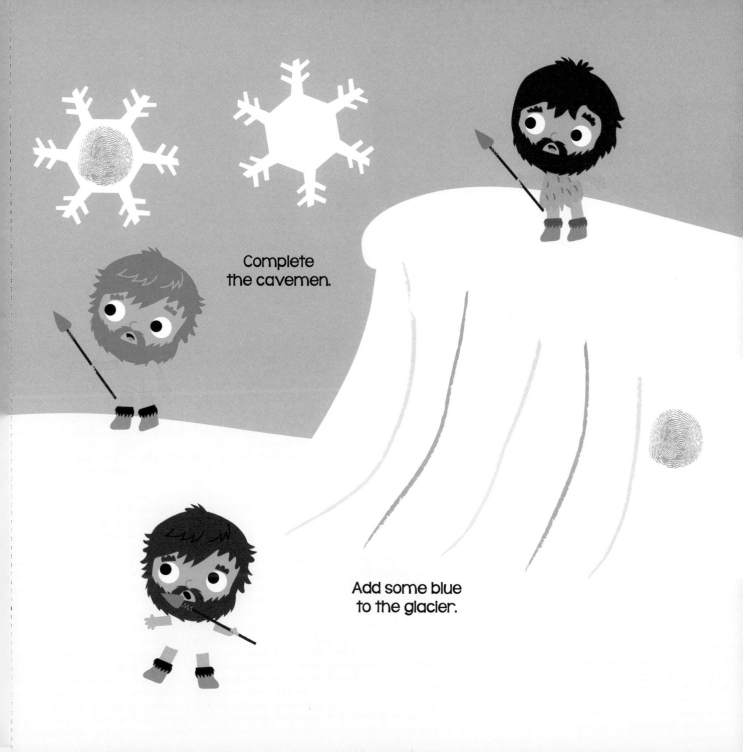

Complete
the cavemen.

Add some blue
to the glacier.

On the farm

Dab your finger in any color and finish coloring the little pigs.

Complete the ducks.

Add some leaves
to these trees.

Dab your finger
in the red paint and
add some apples.

Finish the sheep
and add spots
on the cows.

Add some colors to the sail.

At the beach

Finish coloring the sun with your thumb.

Add some colored fingerprints on the beach ball and bucket.

Color in all the sails on the boats using your thumb.

Complete the seashells with the right color.

In the sky

Finish the seagulls.

Add different colored
fingerprints on the
hot air balloon.

Color in the helicopter
with your fingerprints.

Use your finger
to dab the paint and
color the plane's wing.

In the jungle

Dab your finger in the paint to complete the lions.

Add spots on the giraffe.

Complete the ostriches.

The crocodiles

Color the crocodiles and their eggs.

Color in
the flowers.

Halloween

Color in
the witches.

Finish
the broom.

Color in
the pumpkin.

Dab your fingerprints on the monsters.

Color in the moon.

Draw beautiful pumpkins, using 3 fingerprints for each.

Happy Birthday!

Add fingerprints on the balloons and presents.

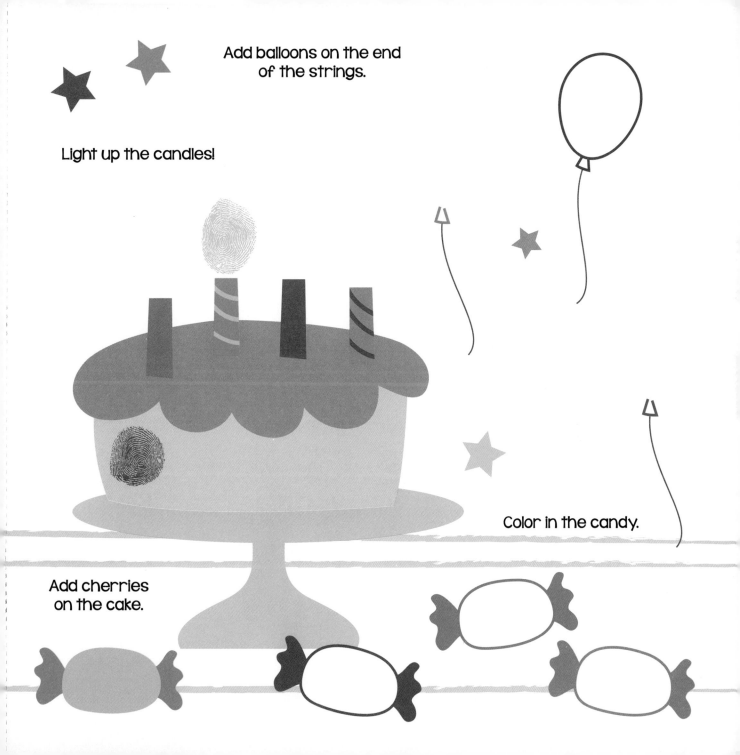

Add balloons on the end
of the strings.

Light up the candles!

Color in the candy.

Add cherries
on the cake.

The pool

Color the slide
with your fingerprints.

Add your colored fingerprints on
the air mattress and on the beach balls.

Add colored circles
on the beach towels.

Dab your thumb in the yellow paint
to add sand around the pool.

Ants and ladybugs

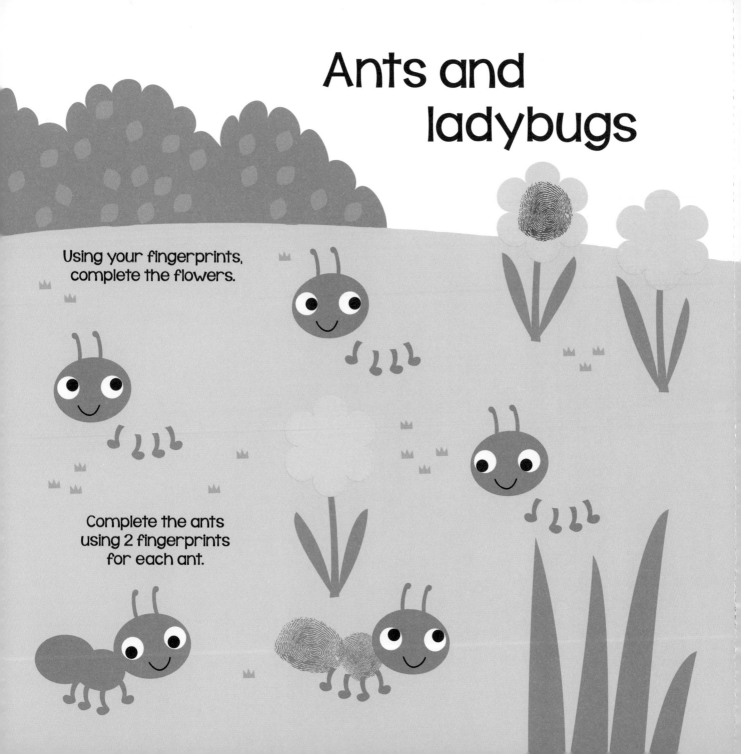

Using your fingerprints, complete the flowers.

Complete the ants using 2 fingerprints for each ant.

Dab your finger in the yellow paint
and finish coloring the sun.

Complete the ladybugs
by adding spots
with your small finger.

The pirates

Using your fingerprints, color the windows and the sail.

Color the fish with your thumb.

Finish
the pirates.

Color the golden
coins.

In the forest

Dab your finger in paint and complete the mushrooms.

Complete the bear cubs.

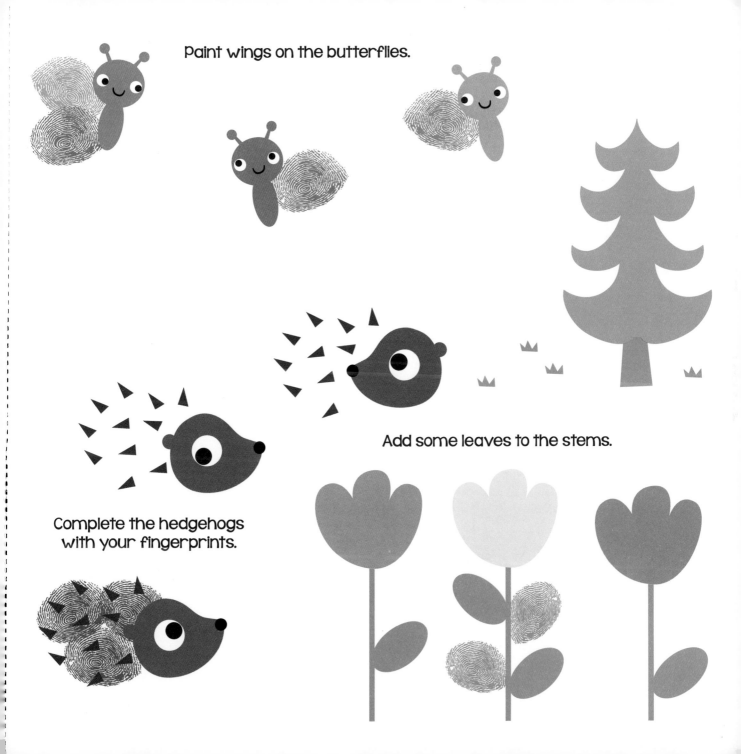

Paint wings on the butterflies.

Add some leaves to the stems.

Complete the hedgehogs
with your fingerprints.

The kittens

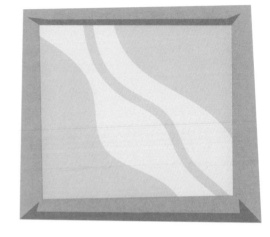

Put some spots all over the beanbag.

Complete all the kittens.

Add some color
to the curtains.

Color the balls of wool,
using your finger.

Color in the rug with your fingerprints.

Winter!

Finish the snowflakes with your fingerprints.

Complete the snowmen.

Add colored balls on the Christmas tree.

Ducks

Color their shelter, using your fingerprints.

Draw bodies on the ducklings with your fingerprints.

Pick beautiful colors
for the flowers.

Goodbye!

Color in the wheels.

Add some clouds.

This minibus needs some colors!